I'm Alive!

How I Breathe

First published in 1991 by Firefly Books Limited.

This edition published in 1993 by Wayland (Publishers) Ltd.

This revised edition published in 2009 by Wayland,
338 Euston Road, London NW1 3BH.

Wayland Australia
Level 17/207 Kent Street, Sydney, NSW 2000

Consultant: Jane Battell

British Library Cataloguing in Publication Data
Suhr, Mandy
How I breathe.–(I'm alive)
1. Respiration–Pictorial works–Juvenile literature.
2. Air–Pictorial works–Juvenile literature.
3. Air–Pollution–Pictorial works–Juvenile literature.
I. Title II. Series III. Gordon, Mike.
612.2'1-dc22

ISBN 9780750259477

Printed in China

Wayland is a division of Hachette Children's Books,
an Hachette UK company.

www.hachette.co.uk

How I Breathe

Written by Mandy Suhr
Illustrated by Mike Gordon

WAYLAND

When I was a tiny baby inside
my mummy, she helped me to breathe.

As soon as I was born I
started to breathe on my own.
I am breathing all the time.

People and most animals breathe air.
We can't see or feel air, but it is all around us.

Air is a mixture of gases. One of these gases is called oxygen. The muscles in our bodies need oxygen from the air to work.

When I breathe air in through my nose,
the oxygen begins its journey to my muscles.

The air goes down a pipe into
my lungs. Their job is to
take the oxygen out of
the air and pass it
to my blood.

Then my blood
takes the oxygen
around my body
to my muscles.

9

The parts of the air that I don't need are pushed out of my lungs, back up the pipe and out of my mouth. This is breathing out!

As you breathe in, and your lungs fill with air, your chest gets bigger.

Your chest gets smaller again as you breathe out.

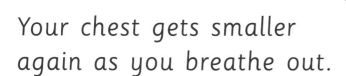

Sometimes, when I'm running or playing football, my muscles need to work harder and so they need more oxygen.

Then I have to breathe faster
to get more air into my lungs.

Plants breathe through their leaves! You can't see them do it, though.

Plants don't have muscles that need oxygen but they do need other gases in the air to help them to grow.

Most animals breathe air in the same way that we do. Stan, my dog, needs oxygen for his muscles, just like I do.

Fish don't breathe air like we do, but they do need oxygen. They have a special way of taking it from the water that they live in.

19

So you can see how important clean air is. Dirty or smoky air makes our lungs dirty and then they can't work so well.

Dirty air makes plant's leaves dirty and then they can't breathe and they die.

We must look after our air.
These things all make our
air dirty.

Can you think of
any other ways to
keep our air clean?

NO

SMOKING

Notes for Adults

I'm Alive is a series of first information books particularly suitable for the early and emergent stages of reading.

Each book in the series inlcudes simple, factual text, and amusing and colourful illustrations, to combine reading for pleasure with fact-finding.

The series takes a closer look at the human body and how it works and develops, comparing this with other forms of life. **I'm Alive** is designed to address the requirements of the National Curriculum for Science at key stage 1.

The books are equally suitable for use at school or at home.
Below are some suggestions for extension activities that can be carried out with children to complement and extend the learning in this book.

Extension Activities

1 Blow up a balloon. Watch how the rubber expands as the air is forced into it. Your lungs are like two balloons, they expand as they fill with air. Feel your chest expanding as you breathe in.

2 Time yourself running around for one, two and three minutes. Notice what happens to your breathing after each time you run around. Make a chart to show your results.

3 When air has become dirty, we say it is 'polluted'. Make posters to advertise ways of stopping pollution. How many ways can you think of?

24